Mum and Dad went shopping.

2

Kipper bought a balloon.

They went to the supermarket.

The balloon went bang.

Kipper bought a new balloon.

Dad went to the toilet.

Dad saw a balloon.

"Kipper's balloon!" he said.

10

Dad ran after it.

The balloon flew away.

Dad chased it.

The balloon was on a statue.

Dad got it down.

"Oh no!" said Dad.